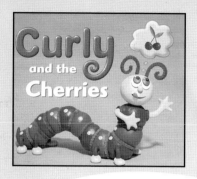

Curly and the **Cherries**

Will Curly get the cherries?

W~~alkthrough~~

Th~~is~~

Th~~e~~
cal~~~~
ab~~~~
car~~~~

This is the title.

Read the title, pointing to each word in turn. Point out the letter 'c' and digraph 'ch'.

Walkthrough

This is the back cover.

This is the blurb. The blurb tells us something about the story. Let's read it.

'Will Curly get the cherries?'

Does the picture give you a clue?

Walkthrough

This is the title page.

Read the title with the children, pointing to each word in turn.

What is happening in the picture?

What do you think the wasp is doing?

What do you think will happen in the story?

1

Walkthrough

This story is told in pictures only. The only words are on the cover and the title page.

Where are the cherries growing?

Where is Curly?

What is Curly trying to do?

What could happen next?

 Observe and Prompt

Language Comprehension

Check that children:

- are looking at everything in the picture
- notice that this is one picture
- can identify the characters
- can predict what might happen next.

Walkthrough

Where is Curly now?

What is he trying to do?

Why should Curly be careful?

What do you think the wasps are doing? Why?

5

 Observe and Prompt

Language Comprehension

Check that children:
- notice the change in the picture
- note the importance of the wasps
- can predict what might happen next.

Walkthrough

What is different about these pages?
(*two separate pictures*)

What is Curly trying to do?

Why are the wasps watching Curly?

Walkthrough

What has happened?

Why do you think Curly has fallen?

How do you think the wasps feel?

 Observe and Prompt

Language Comprehension

Check that children:

- understand that the two pages depict different events
- can predict what might happen next.

Walkthrough

What has happened?

Where is Curly?

Why is he smiling?

👁 **Observe and Prompt**

Language Comprehension

Check that children:

- can describe Curly's feelings after the fall
- notice how the story was built up and concluded.

8